YOU'RE THE V...
Dusty Springfield

© 2006 by International Music Publications Ltd
First published by International Music Publications Ltd in 2006
3 Queen Square, London WC1N 3AU
International Music Publications Ltd is a Faber Music company

Editorial, arranging, engraving and recording: Artemis Music Limited (www.artemismusic.com)
Photography: BBC / Redferns Music Picture Library
Printed in England by Caligraving Ltd
All rights reserved

ISBN 0-571-52502-4

To buy Faber Music publications or to find out about the full range of titles available,
please contact your local music retailer or Faber Music sales enquiries:

Faber Music Ltd, Burnt Mill, Elizabeth Way, Harlow, CM20 2HX England
Tel: +44(0)1279 82 89 82
Fax: +44(0)1279 82 89 83
sales@fabermusic.com fabermusic.com

RESPECT
THE VALUE OF
MUSIC

Dusty Springfield
1939-1999
'White Lady Of Soul'

Dusty Springfield is undoubtedly one of the greatest female vocalists to emerge from the UK. Her soulful vocals, versatility and collaborations with established songwriters including Burt Bacharach and Diane Warren, have proved to be a winning combination. Between 1963 and 1969, Dusty made the UK chart seventeen times, hitting the Top Ten ten times. In 1966 'You Don't Have To Say You Love Me' stayed at number 1 in the UK chart for an astounding thirteen weeks.

Born Mary O'Brien, as a child Dusty was surrounded by jazz and blues and listened to a wide range of music including Gershwin, Rodgers and Hart, Rodgers and Hammerstein, Cole Porter, Count Basie, Duke Ellington and Glen Miller. At the age of ten, when convent-educated Dusty was asked what she wanted to become by her teachers, she answered: "I want to be a blues singer!"

Before Dusty established herself as a solo artist, she recorded and performed with The Lana Sisters, and later with the 'jolly and loud singing' commercial folk band, The Springfields. They enjoyed success on both sides of the Atlantic, but were eventually were caught between the tensions of pop and folk, which prompted Dusty to leave the group and pursue her passion for American Black Music.

In 1964 Dusty released her debut single 'I Only Want To Be With You', which achieved gold status in the UK, and became a major hit in the US. Dusty was a strong influence in the British invasion of the American Charts, along with The Beatles and The Rolling Stones. Chart success continued for the 'Top World Female Artist' award winner (NME) with the release of the album *Where Am I Going* (1967), the title of the album perhaps reflecting her increasing dissatisfaction with her work.

Fortunately, a change of record company to Atlantic records and a new songwriting team breathed new life into her work, and delivered Dusty's critically acclaimed album *Dusty In Memphis* (1969). This was her opportunity to show her true colours to the musical world. Although the album was not a huge seller, only reaching 43 in the UK charts, it is recognized as one of the greatest albums of the decade, producing the huge single 'Son Of A Preacher Man', which hit number 9 in the UK and number 10 in the USA charts in December 1968.

The 70s saw Dusty relocate to the USA as record sales faded; however she continued to release albums including *From Dusty With Love* in 1970, *See All Her Faces* (1972), *Cameo* (1973) and *It Begins Again* (1978).

In 1987, Dusty stormed back into the charts, duetting with The Pet Shop Boys on the number 2 hit 'What Have I Done To Deserve This'. Dusty's soulful attributes contrasted well with the Pet Shop Boys' almost vacant style, and introduced Dusty to a new generation.

Tragically, in 1995 Dusty was diagnosed with terminal breast cancer. Before her death aged 59 on 2nd March 1999, she was honoured with an OBE in the New Years Honours List, and shortly after her death was inducted into the Rock And Roll Hall Of Fame.

"Dusty Springfield is one of the greatest singers and interpreters of song of our time. She not only sings the song – she lives the song." Carole King

ALL I SEE IS YOU

Words and Music by Ben Weisman and Clive Westlake

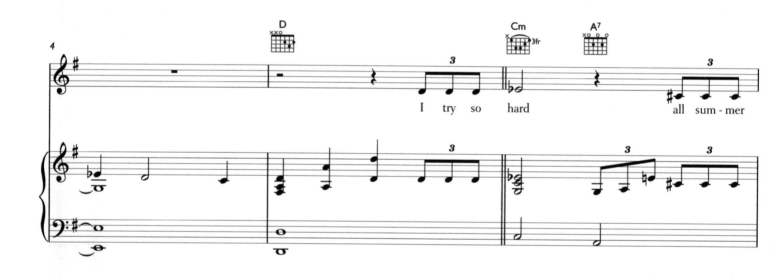

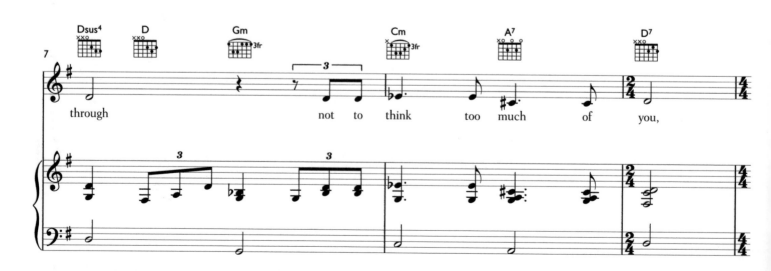

GOIN' BACK

Words and Music by Carole King and Gerry Goffin

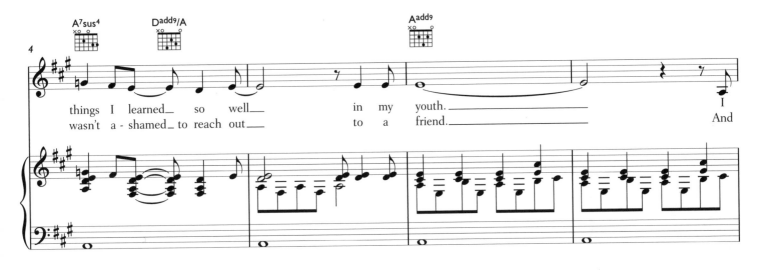

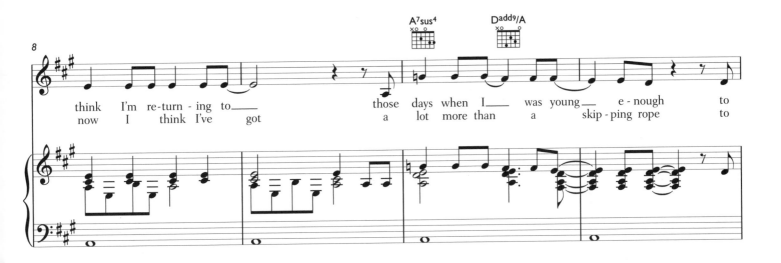

I CLOSE MY EYES AND COUNT TO TEN

Words and Music by Clive Westlake

I JUST DON'T KNOW
WHAT TO DO WITH MYSELF

Words by Hal David
Music by Burt Bacharach

Medium slow

1. I just don't know what to do with my-self. Don't know
(2.) know what to do with my time, I'm so

just what to do with my-self. I'm so used to do - ing
lone-some for you it's a crime. Go-ing to a mov - ie

I ONLY WANT TO BE WITH YOU

Words and Music by Mike Hawker and Ivor Raymonde

THE LOOK OF LOVE

Words by Hal David
Music by Burt Bacharach

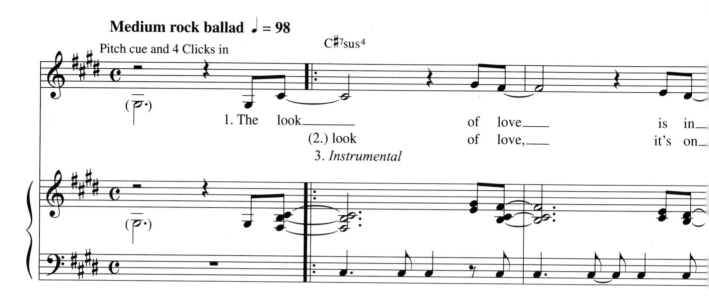

LOSING YOU

Words and Music by Tom Springfield and Clive Westlake

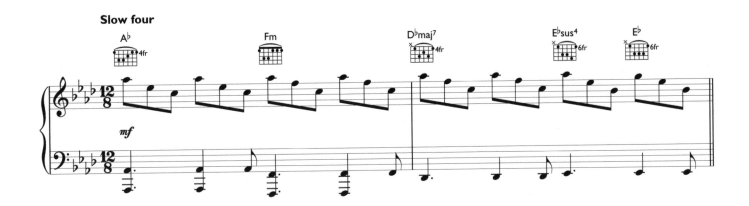

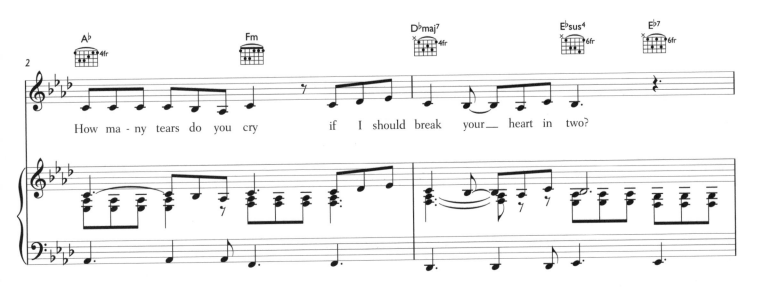

How ma-ny tears do you cry   if I should break your__ heart in two?

How ma-ny tears will I cry   now that I know I'm__ los-ing you?   I

32

SOME OF YOUR LOVIN'

Words and Music by Carole King and Gerry Goffin

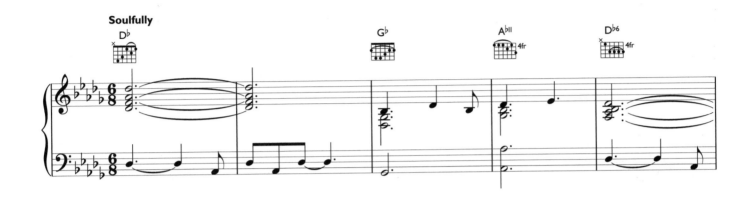

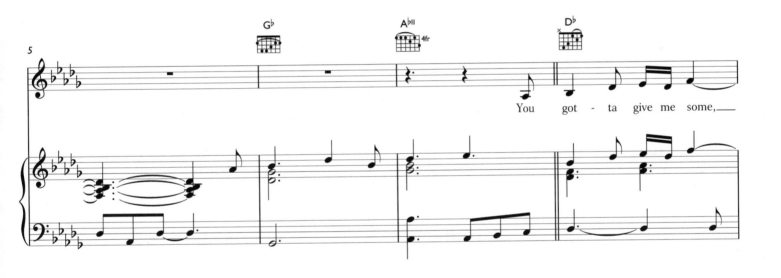

SON OF A PREACHER MAN

Words and Music by John Hurley and Ronnie Wilkins

YOU DON'T HAVE TO SAY YOU LOVE ME

Original Words by Vito Pallavicini
English Words by Simon Napier-Bell and Vicki Wickham
Music by Pino Donaggio